BRITAIN'S HERITAGE

The Slate Industry

Anthony Coulls

AMBERLEY

Acknowledgements

I would like to thank Lynn C. Francis, Principal Archivist for Gwynedd Archives Service for permission to use material from Slatesite (www.llechicymru.info) particularly relating to the Penrhyn and Assheton-Smith families. Grateful thanks to Ann Hatherill for her generosity in allowing use of her photograph collection, without which, the book would be very much poorer. Also, great appreciation to Pred Hughes, Peter Johnson, Clare Oates, Jamie Field, Bob Gwynne and Colin Harris for photographs provided, as well as my father, Peter Coulls, for scanning services and providing his own pictures and those from the late Tom Charman. Several of the images were taken by the author over the last twenty-three years. In addition, I am grateful to Dr David Gwyn who proof-read the text.

This book is dedicated to all those who sparked and supported my interest in the slate industry over forty years, including my parents, wife and daughters – all of whom have been dragged up quarry landscapes – as well as the amazing people I have met along the way, like Dr Michael Lewis, Dr David Gwyn, Dr Gwynfor Pierce-Jones, Dafydd Price, Griff Jones, Pred Hughes and the Plas Tan y Bwlch team. MRFS and Gary Boyd-Hope also deserve special mention for our initial explorations of quarries in the 1990s, when we struck out from our volunteering on the Talyllyn Railway.

First published 2019

Amberley Publishing
The Hill, Stroud
Gloucestershire, GL5 4EP

www.amberley-books.com

Copyright © Anthony Coulls, 2019

The right of Anthony Coulls to be identified as the Author of this work has been asserted in accordance with the Copyrights, Designs and Patents Act 1988.

ISBN 978 1 4456 9105 3 (paperback)
ISBN 978 1 4456 9106 0 (ebook)

British Library Cataloguing in Publication Data. A catalogue record for this book is available from the British Library.

Typesetting by Aura Technology and Software Services, India. Printed in the UK.

Contents

1
Introduction – Roofing the World

For a period in the nineteenth century, ships exported thousands of tons of roofing slate from the UK to an international market. The slate industry has a long and fascinating history, and this book looks at the various aspects, including a brief explanation of the formation of the rock and the properties that make it so suitable as a roofing material. Many other slate products have been made as well, including writing slates, electrical installations and even snooker tables. Slate craft as an art form is also something we shall cover in the book. The material is synonymous with North Wales, where a bid for World Heritage Site status is being made for the landscape formed by quarrying, but the intention is also to look at the slates of Leicestershire, Cornwall and Cumbria. While much of the book covers Wales due to the sheer size of the industry in that country, and the author's familiarity with the region, the processes, products and transport of slate are universal and will be covered along with the life and communities of the quarrymen. It is also true that slate is found internationally, French, American and Spanish slate being particularly of note, but beyond the scope of these pages. Finally, the book looks at the enormous physical remains of the quarries themselves, sometimes developed as tourist attractions and at other times left as landscape features ripe for exploration and discovery.

Slate is a sedimentary rock. It's impossible to write about it without a short session on geology, the study of rocks and minerals. The tectonic environment for producing

A view down the exit incline from the Rhiwbach Tramway on a December afternoon in 1997 reveals the then still-working Maenofferen quarry at the base and the Vale of Ffestiniog beyond, the impact of slate on the landscape being clearly evident.

While cities across the world have vast expanses of buildings roofed with slate, even small towns and villages show the legacy of the industry. This is Fairbourne, on the Cambrian coast, taken from the tips of the Goleuwern quarry above the village. Even the modern bungalows have slate roofs.

slate is usually a former sedimentary basin that becomes involved in a convergent plate boundary. Shales and mudstones in that basin are compressed by horizontal forces with minor heating. These forces and heat modify the clay minerals in the shale and mudstone. Foliation develops at right angles to the compressive forces of the convergent plate boundary to yield a vertical foliation that usually crosses the bedding planes that existed in the shale. Laid down in layers, it consists of mainly clay minerals or micas, depending upon the degree of metamorphism to which it has been subjected. The original clay minerals in shale alter to micas with increasing levels of heat and pressure. Slate can also contain abundant quartz and small amounts of feldspar, calcite, pyrite, hematite and other minerals. And the layering, otherwise known as foliation, makes it ideal for splitting into sheets down what are known as cleavage planes. The properties of slate are that it is hard wearing and also it's a good insulator, making it ideal for electrical installations. However, it's for roofing that slate is most widely known internationally, many civic buildings in Australia having Welsh slate roofs. One can often date buildings in a townscape by looking to see which have tiles and which are more recent, roofed with slates after the production and transport of them became simpler and more widespread. Look at any image of a nineteenth-century townscape with rows and rows of terraced houses and the roofs will uniformly be of English or Welsh slate, a very impressive sight and testament to the thousands of tons produced at the industry's peak.

Did you know?

The first recorded slate roof of a private home is reported to be in North Wales around 1300. For most people, the material was too expensive and could usually only be found on castles or other military structures.

Slate in the UK is generally thought of as a Welsh or Cumbrian material; however, there are some very large workings of it in Cornwall and even in the Midlands around the Swithland area of Leicestershire. It varies in colour too, although it is so often simply thought of as being grey; a short time in slate-working regions will show that the rock will show a green, blue or even purple hue. Where the three occur relatively closely, some incredible slate art manifests itself in roofs, and some builders will specify what colour they wish according to taste. In Cumbria, the Burlington slate is known as 'blue-grey' and asked for as such. Despite being found internationally, in the USA and France in particular, slate from the UK has been used across the world for nearly 200 years. Its origins in use go back much further; the Romans knew of the properties of slate in locations such as the Nantlle Valley, though it would take time for this to spread even in the North Wales region, Blaenau Ffestiniog slate being found in 1755 by Methusalem Jones. As the nineteenth century progressed, quarrymen from Blaenau moved south into Meirionydd and opened the quarries around Corris, Talyllyn and the surrounding area. Welsh workers moved south to Pembrokeshire and thence on further to Cornwall and Cumbria to work alongside the industry's existing outlets in those locations.

Returning to the beginnings of slate in Wales in particular, the fort at Segontium (Caernarfon) originally had tiled roofs, which were replaced at a later date with slate. Some of the floors were made of slate slabs in the fourth century. But slate was also used in a much earlier Roman fort at Caer Llugwy, between Capel Curig and the Conwy Valley, two centuries before. Slate was used for roofing the eight towers of Conwy Castle between 1283 and 1287. Indeed, during the Welsh wars of independence, Edward I of England, while visiting the copper mines of Drws y Coed, is reputed to have stayed at a house in the Nantlle Valley roofed with slates from the Cilgwyn quarry. In 1317, the great hall of Llywelyn II (Llywelyn the Last) was removed from Conwy to Caernarfon Castle and slated by one Henry le Sclatiere.

Around 1358–60, building repairs were carried out at Chester, under the supervision of the Black Prince, when 'slate stones' were bought for the roof of the great stable at Chester Castle.

John Leland during his travels between 1536 and 1539 remarked that 'the houses withyn the town of Oswestre be of tymbre and slated' and at Is Dulas, on the eastern side of the River Dulas in Denbighshire, 'they dig oute slate stones to kyver houses.' Slates were also used on houses in Wrexham during the reign of Elizabeth I. During the episcopacy of William Morgan (translator of the Bible into Welsh) at St Asaph (1601–04) the cathedral chancel was slated. In 1682, more slating with Penrhyn slates took place and during renovation in the 1930s, these slates, which were by then over 250 years old, were strong enough to be re-used on new timbers.

Slate is not solely a Welsh preserve, the rock being found from Cornwall to Scotland. In the Midlands, it was quarried in the Swithland area of Leicestershire, as shown in this partially flooded working.

The Nantlle Valley of North Wales was worked in Roman times for slate and the view of quarries down the valley from Pen yr Orsedd betrays that long history, looking towards the Pen y Bryn and Dorothea quarries.

Another early slate roof of note was Plas y Gogarth, near Llandudno. This was owned by the Bishop of Bangor, and was roofed in the thirteenth century. All in all, the picture we have is of slates being used on the better kind of house in North Wales at this time, a time which saw a great deal of building activity. Slates from the Glyn Ceiriog area were available in 1675. However, it must be kept in mind that apart from castles and cathedrals, it was not uncommon in Wales to use slates for roofing at this time. Any transportation involved the use of ships. Indeed, the chief export of the area by Tudor times was slate, as up to 1603, there are references of slate being exported from Aberogwen (Bangor), to Dublin and Carlingford in Ireland as well as the Foryd (Rhyl), St Asaph and Chester. Slates from Pembrokeshire were exported to the south-east coast of Ireland as well as Bristol. It is also interesting to note that slates shipped through Antwerp were imported into London in 1567 to re-roof the Royal Exchange. More recently, Welsh slate was used to roof the Palace of Westminster in the nineteenth century, for the electricity panels of the Cunard liners *Queen Mary* and *Queen Elizabeth* in the 1930s, as a damp course for the new cathedral at Guildford in 1960 as well as re-roofing the whole of Downing Street in 1962–63.

By comparison with the Welsh iron, coal, copper and lead industries, the slate industry was very primitive as late as 1750, even though 2 million slates appear to have been exported from Caernarfon in the 1730s. By 1790, slates were exported not only to various Welsh ports, but to at least eighteen English ports, ten Irish ports and two Scottish ports, apart from Boulogne, Dunkirk and Rotterdam on mainland Europe. Substantial development was very slow. By 1832, the annual output of slates from the North Wales quarries was 100,000 tons. By 1882 it was over 450,000 tons, only to decline by 1972 to about 22,000 tons. The slate industry reached its dramatic zenith in a very short period. Its decline was just as dramatic. Up to around 1750 all the Welsh slate quarries were very small and shallow excavations and were worked by local people for their own individual needs or for sale. This had been happening for centuries.

Pembrokeshire had its own quarries, on a smaller scale than North Wales but no less significant for the communities around. This is part of the Rosebush workings on the southern slopes of the Preseli hills.

In Cumbria, it was a similar position. There is evidence of its use from the time of the Romans – at their fort at Hardknott for example – through to important buildings such as Calder Abbey in medieval times. Outcrops of slate on the surface would be the source initially, developing into open quarries, although later the 'metal' would be mined underground via a level driven through to the vein.

The massive expansion of the industry through the eighteenth and nineteenth centuries was in response to the demand for slate roofing as a result of the growth of industrial towns in Ireland and northern England. It depended, however, on two factors influencing supply – an effective transport system away from the quarries and mines, and advances in technology within them.

Horse and human power were the prime movers initially, transporting the riven and dressed slates by cart or sledge down to water. This could be a relatively short journey, such as that down to ships waiting on the Duddon Sands from the Kirkby Moor quarries above. Or it could be a long and arduous trek. Honister was linked by a graded pack horse route (called Moses' Trod after a famous quarryman) over the high fells to reach the shores of Wasdale and then eventually the coast at Ravenglass or Drigg some 14 miles or so away. Slate from the Troutbeck Park quarries was similarly taken down to Windermere, along the lake to Waterfoot, overland to Haverthwaite and then by lighter to ships at Greenodd or Ulverston. Mass movement depended on the arrival of the railway, for example the Coniston branch of the Furness Railway in 1859, although many locations like Honister were still remote from the nearest railhead and would rely on motor transport.

Did you know?

At Collyweston in Northamptonshire is a mine that has been called a slate mine for decades, however the stone that is worked is limestone found in narrow beds. It's much heavier than true slate but has found local use for roofing and the mine recently reopened to help repair part of King's College, Cambridge.

2
Winning and Working the Slate

The nature of slate as a sedimentary rock means it must be carefully worked to minimise waste and use good stone to the best possible ends. Even the very act of removing it from Mother Earth must be managed and undertaken in a way such that damage is minimal. There are three basic forms of slate quarry, dependent on the geology of the slate veins where the rock occurs. Where it dips sharply away from the surface, an open pit such as Hodge Close in Cumbria, Delabole in Cornwall, Swithland in Leicestershire or Dorothea in North Wales results. Slate occurring close to the surface but underground in the manner of Carnglaze, Honister or the Ffestiniog district of North Wales results in true mining in caverns and galleries or floors, while where the seam of slate is at surface, galleries working the rock in open formation up a hillside are the result. Some locations have a mixture of pit and gallery, such as some of Dinorwig and Penrhyn, but the product from each is the same.

The challenge of working the rock is also identical despite how it may be won. The slate has to be extracted somehow, and while powder is used to blast pieces off the working face, the quarryman will have understood the face first and identified the piece of stone he required. Before electricity, steam or compressed air, the holes for the explosive charges were drilled by hand using a special metal rod called a jumper. The rod was repeatedly beaten into the rock and turned, as a drill would be, and eventually a hole for the charge would result. If you wanted a particular piece of rock, then a pattern of holes meant that ideally a section of stone would be loosened and could be removed in a large section for working to quality. The way of the rock, its qualities and location in a quarry was borne of knowledge and familiarity. Experience could not be taught in a college, and father passed that

The deep pit of Delabole in Cornwall demonstrates the method of working that sees an open excavation driven deeper and deeper in search of the vein of slate. The exit road from the bottom can be seen as it zig-zags its way to the mills level at the top of the pit.

Above: Underground workings are found in many Welsh quarries around Blaenau Ffestiniog. Pred Hughes took this photo of the partially flooded chamber one on the East Old Vein of Cwmorthin, illustrating the conditions men had to work in.

Left: Galleries on a hillside are very visual representations of an industry, decades after work has ended. Dinorwic quarry closed in 1969 but the effect on the landscape is still clear after five decades. It is this unique landscape that has seen the slate region of North Wales put forward for World Heritage Site status.

Above: The massive Penrhyn quarry combined both pit and gallery working, though the pit is now flooded. Still operational, the quarry has also diversified, and the lines of the mile-long zip wire can be seen crossing the photograph.

Below: Of the giant quarries, Dinorwic also combined pit and gallery. Rock was lifted out of the pits using aerial ropeways nicknamed 'Blondins' after the famous tightrope walker. In September 2018, some relics of these still remain in the quarry, and on the galleries many blast shelters also still stand.

Left: This picture shows the reality of the life of a rockman, clinging on to the rock face held by rope and driving the jumper rod into the stone to prepare for blasting. Neither power assistance nor protective clothing was available and the men carried out this work in all weathers.

Below: The marks of a jumper can clearly be seen in an underground chamber in Cwmorthin – this method was used both on the surface and below ground.

intuition to son and so on throughout the generations. While there were textbooks published on the science of mining, this was no substitute for knowing the rock and understanding it. In Wales, quarrymen tended to work as a team of four: two rockmen working on extracting a block from the quarry, either underground or on the surface, and their partners in the splitting and dressing mills on the surface. The team leader and the quarry owner's agent would meet periodically to agree the working price for each lot, known as a 'bargain', the team's pay being governed by the monthly output of finished slates.

This sub-contracting system gave rise to a form of universal credit, everyone in debt to somebody. Weekly loans were available from the management, to be offset against the next monthly pay, but injury, sickness, bad weather or poor rock could upset any attempt at planned spending. The bargain system was common to the entire slate industry. The debt, insecurity, favouritism, poverty and general discontent leading from it led to the formation of the North Wales Quarrymen's Union in 1874. Their time of trial would come at the turn of the century, as shall be seen in a coming chapter.

Men climbed rock faces with minimal safety equipment and a chain wrapped around one leg provided secure footing for a rockman. Film taken as late as the 1960s shows workers climbing a face quickly and securely in a way that would be frowned upon today but was accepted practice for decades. Blasting was an activity that would happen once a day, timed to allow for dust to settle and the rock to then be removed for working. There would also then be time for the rockmen to return with jumpers and drills to prepare for the next charge. Larger quarries had blasting shelters where the men would retreat to until the explosion had been carried out. Similar to wartime bomb shelters, these were solidly constructed with minimal doors and windows. Even today, many survive on the various levels of the massive Dinorwig quarry – different to the caban, examined late in the book, but just as much appreciated.

The first task in processing the slate was to remove slabs after blasting; here a slab can be seen being hoisted onto a small railway trolley for transport to the mill.

Ann and Gordon Hatherill recorded the slate industry in great detail during the 1970s. This, one of their photos, shows slab wagons entering the mill at Llechwedd ready for sawing and splitting, along with some of the finished product alongside.

The dressing of slate from slab to roofing material is an art, and in Wales is best carried out by hand. The individual quarry worker would have his own space in a splitting shed. Welsh quarries of course carried out their business in the Welsh language and a whole host of terms evolved – some very local indeed to the area around the quarry, such as from valley to valley. Slab would be transported to the splitting shed, where first it was sawn to size with a circular saw. Mechanisation and innovation go hand in hand, while dust suppression was a major consideration. In 1852, J. W. Greaves designed powered saw tables to reduce the time taken to process slate, a real consideration in the developing industrial demand for the material. This was followed by the Hunter saw, fabled by some historians, coming to the industry in the 1860s. First developed in Scotland by the Hunters, father and son, in the late 1830s, these rotary saws had renewable tips, reducing the need for a saw doctor, and up to four blades could be accommodated on a single rotary shaft. Used in North Wales and at Delabole in Cornwall, the saw was too rough for many slates, but its use persisted in locations where it suited. In 1996, Hunter saw tips were found in derelict slate mills in Pen Yr Orsedd in the Nantlle Valley. Mills containing quantities of saw tables were built at most quarries, the large Australia Mill derelict at the top level of Dinorwig housing up to sixty saws, with mechanical power transmission and dust extraction systems. The real innovation was the introduction of diamond saw tips in the twentieth century, which first appeared in 1925 and were universal by the 1970s in all the quarries then working across the country.

Splitting the slate is the ultimate demonstration of the quarryman's skill to create the finished product for roofing. Indeed, the very origin of the word slate is from the old French verb *esclater*, meaning 'to split'. In southern Meirionydd, a splitting machine invented at Aberllefenni in the nineteenth century was a failure, and while experiments have carried on, the tradition of hand splitting reigned supreme for over 200 years. A simple but well-placed hammer tap on a broad but thin chisel aligned with the natural but invisible grain does the job

An older photo shows the interior of one of the mills at Llechwedd, with Greaves saw tables as far as one can see.

In the 1920s, Dinorwic built a large mill on the Australia level of the quarry (so called because it was so high up and far away). This included central power distribution and dust extraction systems. Slate was brought in by the door at the far end of the mill and the final product was taken out by a door behind the photographer.

Modern mills use diamond-tipped saws similar to this one in use at Llechwedd in the 1970s. It is plain to see that dust suppression has moved on enormously with the blade being kept wet as it cuts.

A working area or 'wal' at Llechwedd in the 1970s still had a wooden bench and hand tools with the rotary dressing machine behind the wal to allow final sizing.

Slate splitting remains a careful hand craft, the initial strokes being the critical part of the operation.

and the slates can be eased apart. This all accompanied with the rock resting on the worker's legs with a simple bench. The mechanised Australia Mill referred to in the last paragraph has all the mechanical saws on one side of the building with a railway track running down it, but on the other side, it is divided into simple individual work spaces, known in Wales as 'wal', where the splitting was undertaken by hand and each man's output measured individually.

Once split, the slate can be dressed to size by hand or mechanically. By hand, the quarryman measures the slate to size, marks it and clefts it manually, at the risk of more wastage and a very laborious process. The innovative John Greaves took inspiration from an agricultural chaff-cutting machine and created a rotary slate dressing machine. His son Richard patented an improved version in 1886 and similar machines are still standard slate dressing equipment in the UK and America to the present day.

Did you know?

Roofing slates are produced in a wide variety of sizes; the system of naming slate sizes after female nobility was devised by General Hugh Warburton at Penrhyn quarry in 1738. It soon became the industry standard and lasted for over two centuries. A roof may well be covered with Empresses, Small Duchesses, Narrow Ladies or even Broad Countesses for example.

The Greaves dresser in action as slate is cut to size for the different needs of the final customer.

Technology crossed counties and countries; this Greaves dresser was among the redundant machines at Honister slate mine in August 2018.

Right: A larger slab of slate, sawn and dressed, is loaded into a Land Rover at Llechwedd. This would not have been for roofing purposes, but will have found a use elsewhere given the versatility of the material.

Below: Outside one of the Llechwedd mills, the slate is stockpiled in different sizes; it can then be easily selected and loaded for market. Note that despite this being taken in the 1970s, narrow gauge railway wagons are still being used for internal transport.

3
Slate on the Move

Many people's introduction to the slate industry is as tourists riding on one of the several narrow-gauge railways in North Wales. Transport is a vital part of the story, but the railway is only one ingredient, and the origins go back before the first lines. Initially, sea and land transport were used, packhorses and ships on the tide. In Cumbria, quarrymen worked laden sleds of slate down the mountainsides by hand until relatively very late – certainly late enough for the practice to be captured on film. Unlike Wales, narrow-gauge railways weren't really an option outside the quarry, though a fearsome tramway existed on Honister Hause and Burlington had an exit railway by 1808. Aerial ropeways were another solution, but road transport held sway in the region, and the larger companies were quick to run their own fleets of steam lorries, moving to petrol and diesel as the twentieth century progressed. With the coming of the main line Cockermouth, Keswick & Penrith Railway, transhipment was easy once on the flat land and sea-bound transport of the slate faded away. Packhorses and road transport were so often the main option for the majority of quarries, though the hazard of damage to the product was great – and another reason why in Wales the narrow-gauge railway was developed and eventually held sway.

Before the slate can be sent to market by road, rail or sea, it must leave the quarry, which may be several hundred feet above the preferred transport system. Many quarries across the UK used inclined railways to lower and raise wagons. The last working incline in the UK was this one at Maenofferen, where two empty wagons have just arrived at the incline head, their working having been balanced by two laden wagons of slate which are now at the foot of the incline for unloading and onward road transport.

Near Porthmadog, the River Dwyryd was the outlet to Cardigan Bay. At no point is the river deep enough to accommodate sea-going ships, but in the second half of the eighteenth century a number of quays were constructed west of Maentwrog, from which small vessels took cargoes of timber and, increasingly, slate to be transferred to sea-going ships in deeper water south-west of what would become Porthmadog, transferring to Porthmadog itself when its harbour was opened in 1824. The river was and remains so shallow that viable cargoes could only be carried at spring tides. Some of the quays remain to this day, used by anglers. In the 1980s one of the small craft used in the transhipment of slate was discovered on the river bed; subsequently excavated and rescued it is a unique survivor from nearly 200 years beforehand. Now displayed at the Welsh Slate Museum, it stands as a symbol from the early industrial period and the first half of the nineteenth century. The opening of the Ffestiniog Railway in 1836 dealt a mortal blow to the Dwyryd traffic, which ended completely by 1860. It was a similar story in Cumbria and Cornwall, though the narrow-gauge railway systems never took off for distribution in the same way in those counties. Internal use of railway lines and small locomotives for transport of slabs and waste was widespread, but the main line railways took on transport to the wider market as the railway mania saw the growth of the railway network in the UK during the nineteenth century. Narrow-gauge railways could conquer terrain at lower capital cost than the standard gauge equivalent and the technology spread worldwide, even if it wasn't to move slate! The building of the Talyllyn Railway in 1864 produced a unique system from quarry to onward distribution as the wharf built in Tywyn was not a sea-facing wharf at all, but a wharf facing on to the Aberystwyth & Welsh Coast Railway.

On the River Dwyryd near Porthmadog is Tyddyn Isa quay. Quiet now, this was once a major location for the transhipment of slate into small vessels which serviced sea-going ships moored in deeper water. The coming of the Ffestinog Railway and the creation of Porthmadog saw the demise of this use, but the quay remains as a monument of industry.

Above: In the Nantlle Valley, the Nantlle Railway for movement of slate was designed and built by George and Robert Stephenson, opening in 1828. Finally closed in 1963, it used horses to pull its trains throughout its existence.

Below: Internal movement of slate at Maenofferen was still carried out by rail in the 1970s, as seen here with a Ruston diesel locomotive moving a trainload of finished slates. They will have been on their way to the incline top to begin their journey to a customer.

Above: The scale of the Dinorwic enterprise can be seen here at the foot of one of the main inclines down to the mills level from the working galleries. Slab wagons, slate wagons and a Hunslet shunting engine are in evidence. The steam engine has a chain attached to the slab wagons to pull them to the foot of the incline.

Below: Opened in 1836, the narrow gauge Ffestiniog Railway first used horses to pull empty trains uphill and the full trains rolled down by gravity, the horse riding in a wagon at the back. In the twenty-first century, gravity trains are run as heritage demonstrations, this one seen leaving Porthmadog early on a May morning in 2017.

Tywyn in southern Meirionydd is home to the Talyllyn Railway, opened in 1864 and using steam locomotives from the outset. One of the original two locomotives, *Talyllyn*, is shown in September 2014 at Wharf station with a selection of restored slate wagons.

The study of these railways in North Wales has spawned many detailed accounts of their histories and operations and one can only refer to these for further information for there is far from enough space in this book to permit much more here.

In the twenty-first century, slate is moved by road, from quarry to workshops and then distribution, the last commercial use of a narrow-gauge railway being at Aberllefenni near Corris until the quarry closed in 2003.

The harbours for sea shipping are also a study in themselves. The great ports of Dinorwig and Port Penrhyn are examples of the largest types of these installations. Penrhyn and Dinorwig ran their own steam ships until 1955, while in Porthmadog many traders set up in business and the town not only spawned these companies but a number of shipyards and ship builders. The very last surviving Porthmadog-built ship was a brig named *Fleetwing*, which survived as a hulk in the Falkland Islands until around 2007. The last ship to trade regularly in and out of Porthmadog worked until 1959, but the last slate shipped from the harbour went in June 1946, while Penrhyn's final shipping of slate went on a Dutch motor coaster in 1962.

The technology of the slate industry also spawned growth in local and regional engineers and foundries supplying both finished machines and components. In Caernarfon, the local timber merchants, De Winton, turned into founders and eventually made locomotives, winches, bridges and all manner of ironwork and general engineering. Many local foundries grew up in the slate-producing regions while surprisingly some of the other transport

Old meets new in the 1970s at Maenofferen as slate wagons are unloaded onto a Leyland lorry for onward transport in a labour-intensive process.

Port Penrhyn in the 1890s was a hive of activity, several vessels being moored for loading, while a pair of Hunslet steam locomotives is busy moving wagons around the quayside.

Port Dinorwic   General View.

The Wrench Series, No. 2257

Port Dinorwic made it onto several postcards of local views, and the closeness of the community to the industry is evident. The supporting activity of engineering and shipwrighting is clear to see from the buildings and chimneys around the docks themselves.

The peak of the slate industry was in the period before the First World War. In this early twentieth-century view, Porthmadog is still busy with sailing ships and the slate stocks are high. In the twenty-first century, the low-roofed building behind the slate is now the Porthmadog Maritime Museum, telling the story of the town's place in international history.

Engineering played a massive role as the slate industry developed. At Penrhyn quarry, the Caernarfon firm of De Winton produced two massive water balance lifts to bring slate out of the pit working and to the mills level. Both remain as monuments to this day.

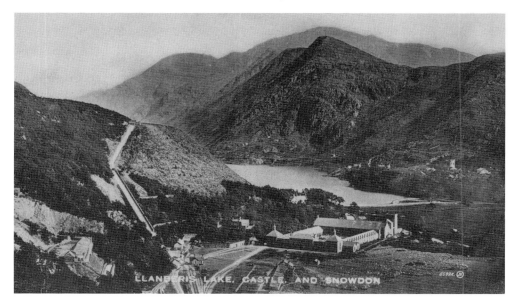

The organised workshops of the Dinorwig quarry at Gilfach Ddu are clear in this postcard view. Note how the caption ignores their existence completely!

Many of the larger quarries were self-sufficient in their maintenance of equipment. With a fleet of steam locomotives, inclines and Blondin hoists, Pen yr Orsedd was no exception, and the workshop complex was remarkable in its completeness in August 1996.

systems such as the Blondins and their associated control gear were made in Scotland by companies such as Henderson. The two biggest Welsh quarries, Dinorwig and Penrhyn, had their own workshops and were pretty much self-sufficient; the museum at Gilfach Ddu in the old Dinorwig works bears this out perfectly with carpentry, brass foundry and machine shop among the facilities. With a fleet of steam locomotives and a massive amount of machinery to support, it was inevitable that such investment would be made.

Did you know?

The Dinorwic company's workshops were built in 1870 in the style of a Canadian frontier fort and operated for nearly a century, being saved for posterity by Gwynedd County Council in 1970 after the quarry closed the previous year.

The electrification of the later surviving working quarries brought in new trades and new equipment, with some very early hydro-electric schemes pioneering the production and use of the new power within the industry. Llechwedd quarry was one of the earliest to go completely electric, even converting its steam shunting locomotives to electric propulsion. The quarry's own power station remains in operation in 2019. Studies have been made and books written on companies and foundries and are well worth reading to see the impact of industrialisation in the mountains, communities and coasts of the quarrying areas – in Cumbria this was also combined with other extractive industries of ores and minerals, as well as coal.

Llechwedd was an innovator in the use of electricity, and even converted two steam locomotives to electric power in the 1920s. In this form, the locomotives were kept working off an overhead power supply into the mid-1970s, as seen here.

Did you know?

In several quarries across the country, aerial ropeways were used to access the deep pits of the workings. Often worked by electricity, these gained the nickname 'Blondins' after the famous tightrope walker of the early twentieth century. The last remaining examples stand as part of the heritage site at Dinorwig and as Scheduled Ancient Monuments at Pen-yr-Orsedd in the Nantlle Valley, though the survival of the latter is more perilous with the passing of each winter.

At Pen yr Orsedd, the skyline was marked by the Blondin ropeway towers, still standing in 1996, twenty years after they last operated. Although Scheduled Ancient Monuments, their survival is precarious given the vagaries of rust and weather.

4

Slate People – the Pioneers, the Investors, the Backers, the Inventors

In the early pages of this book, the name of Methusalem Jones was mentioned as a pioneer of Blaenau Ffestiniog slate. Yet he is but one of dozens of luminaries in the field of slate – from local rockmen to investors from Warwickshire, the slate industry of the United Kingdom attracted individuals from all manner of backgrounds. Then there were the inventors, pushing technological boundaries in the interests of improving production, increasing output and raising quality.

In Blaenau Ffestiniog, the two massive quarries of Llechwedd and Oakley rose to dominance, Llechwedd being the domain of the Greaves family after times of boom and bust, even verging on bankruptcy as investigations for good slate went on. Some owners were diversifying from existing enterprises, William McConnell from the great cotton family in Manchester bought out the Bryn Eglwys quarry in southern Snowdonia to bolster the family finances.

The major players of North Wales were the massive dynasties of Penrhyn and Vaenol. It was Richard Pennant (1737–1808) who first set the industry on its phase of major capital development. Though of Flintshire lineage, Richard Pennant was a Liverpool merchant prince who founded his fortune on the slave trade and inherited estates in Jamaica. On 6 December 1765 he married Ann Susannah, daughter and heiress of General Hugh Warburton (1695–1771), who held part of the moiety of the Penrhyn estate. In 1783, he was raised to the peerage of the Kingdom of Ireland as Baron Penrhyn of Penrhyn in the County of Louth. Holding an Irish peerage, he was not disqualified from sitting in the House of Commons, which he did. This is a brilliant example of the political intrigues that were prevalent in those times. He sat as member for Petersfield from 1761 to 1767, for Liverpool from 1768 to 1780 and again for Liverpool from 1785 to 1790.

He employed as his steward William Williams (1738–1817), who ran the quarry on a purely capitalistic basis, thus permanently changing the infrastructure of the industry. Before his retirement on a pension in 1803 from an indebted Lord Penrhyn, he was to administer efficiently the modes of production, exporting and the selling of slate among many other responsibilities. His contribution cannot be ignored. During this time James Greenfield introduced the now familiar benched gallery system of working the slate resources.

The quarry became a popular tourist attraction, regarded as an example of a spectacular process of the Industrial Revolution and a new wonder of nature developed by man. Princess

Victoria, then thirteen years old, visited the quarry on 8 September 1832, and described the event in her diary:

> It was very curious to see the men split the slate, and others cut it while others hung suspended by ropes and cut the slate; others again drove wedges into a piece of rock and in that manner would split off a block. Then little carts about a dozen at a time rolled down a railway by themselves.

That year, the artist Henry Hawkins painted an oil painting of the quarry in full operation, perhaps as a commemoration for George Dawkins-Pennant – who inherited the estate from Richard, his great-uncle – of the visit and a splendid depiction of the industry in the years before photography.

Did you know?

Penrhyn Castle was built as a fortified manor house in 1438. The profits from the Pennant family's enterprises, including the quarry, enabled it to be rebuilt in a massive neo-Norman style between 1819 and 1834. Now owned by the National Trust, it is as much a monument to industry as the quarry not far away on the estate land.

Penrhyn Castle is a vast monument to the wealth created by the slate industry at its prosperous height and is now open to the public in the ownership of the National Trust.

It was not until 1809 that Thomas Assheton Smith (1752–1828) took over the running of the Dinorwig quarry himself. Indeed, it is important to note the friendship that existed between him and George Hay Dawkins Pennant of Penrhyn, both men being members of the Menai Pitt Club. Following Lord Penrhyn and Sir Watkin Williams-Wynn, he was the third largest landowner in Gwynedd, with 34,000 acres. The annual income from this rental was around £42,000. But the major part of his income came from the Dinorwig quarry, which by 1806 was exporting 20,000 tons of slate. Though at first his father was much more interested in his English estates, and as late as 1792, Faenol was described as 'once the mansion of conviviality and mirth, now the neglected seat of A. Smith, Esq.' However, Thomas Assheton Smith had realised that not only was Faenol of political importance (holding the county seat from 1774 to 1780 and being elected

High Sheriff for 1783–84) but also that the 'tracts of bogs and rocks', as one of his ancestors had called it, did also have some economic possibilities.

From 1778 farms were let on long leases with restrictive clauses to give more security to the tenant and encourage better husbandry. From 1796 Assheton-Smith sat for Andover, Hampshire. It was the slate quarrying industry that was the jewel in the crown and not agriculture (the pioneering pedigree breeding of Welsh Black cattle was to come a century later). Thanks primarily to his support, a scheme to bridge the Menai Strait was thwarted in 1801, and despite violent opposition, when Thomas Assheton Smith had to call for a cavalry unit to protect his interests and quell the rioting, he succeeded in adding 2,692 acres to his estate by enclosing the Common at Llanddeiniolen in 1809.

The dynasties had power and influence, while at the other end of the spectrum were the small quarries scratching out an existence on the hillsides of Wales and Cumbria. The unprofitable Croesor quarry lurched along through the nineteenth century and closed between 1878 and 1882. In 1895, the quarry reopened under the direction of Moses Kellow, a fearless innovator who set about modernising working practices and methods. The two-man teams working in the mill were no longer tied to a two-man team working underground, which enabled the mill to operate more efficiently. Following trials with air drills, he decided instead to electrify the mill, building a large hydro-electric station, which generated three-phase alternating current, rather than the direct current recommended by British manufacturers. He obtained motors from Prague, which were used to drive winches and an electric locomotive, the first to work in Wales. The water wheels were supplemented by Pelton wheels, supplied by Gilbert Gilkes of Kendal. His greatest innovation was the Kellow drill, a hydraulic drill for which he obtained six patents between 1898 and 1915. It could drill a 7.5-foot (2.3 m) hole in the slate in under two minutes, much less than the day required using hand drills. Some personalities came later of course. In Cumbria, Honister's owners initially in the nineteenth century were fairly unremarkable and the quarry occupied a fairly humdrum existence, closing as so many others did without being marked. The input of the entrepreneurial Mark Weir, who reopened the quarry in 1997, not only re-equipped the facilities but enhanced the site as a tourist attraction. He was lively and imaginative and very much a character, who celebrated the past of the Cumbrian industry while developing Honister and making it sustainable.

The Liberal MP for Southern Meirionydd in Wales, Sir Henry Haydn Jones bought the Bryn Eglwys quarry around 1911 and kept it open with subsidies from his own pocket until 1946. Stories and individuals across the country told similar tales; the industry was a hard one to make a living from, and speculating was high risk indeed. The number of small scratchings and exploratory workings across the country runs into the hundreds, but comparatively very few were commercially successful for any great length of time.

The boom and bust fragile nature of the industry is summed up in Meirionydd just outside Porthmadog, where stands the impressive three-storied Ynys-y-pandy slate processing works. Serving the Gorseddau quarry, it was built in 1856–7. It is ingeniously planned so that the natural fall of the site assisted the manufacturing process. A deep trench inside accommodated a large overshot water wheel, and on the south side a long curving embankment brought branches of the tramway from Gorseddau quarry into the mill at two different levels, serving the middle and upper floors. The grand round-headed openings are closely spaced like a Roman aqueduct. The eastern gable is surmounted by a decorative feature incorporating a false chimney stack, and the west gable windows have at some time had window frames or shutters. Otherwise the construction is bold and plain but none the less impressive.

Right: Mark Weir took the derelict Honister mine in 1997 and reopened it, diversifying and making it attractive to all comers. This is part of the Visitor Centre in August 2018.
Below: Sir Henry Haydn Jones bought Bryn Eglwys quarry in 1911 and ran it until 1946. This view shows the launder, which would have taken water to run a waterwheel for power and the manager's house to the right. Taken in 1975, the buildings have since been demolished.

The mill specialised in the production of slate slabs for floors, dairies, troughs, urinals, etc. In its heyday, in 1860, it was producing over 2,000 tons per annum, but seven years later production was down to 25 tons per annum (due to the poor quality of the quarried slate) and the business went into liquidation in 1871. The building provided a venue for eisteddfodau cultural festivals until the roof was removed around 1906 and it now stands a proud monument, a cathedral of slate unparalleled anywhere.

Ynysypandy Mill with the Gorseddau Quarry it served in the distance. Connected by a tramway whose tracks ran into the mill on the embankment seen, the mill worked for under twenty years but stands as an incredible memorial to the investment put into the industry in the nineteenth century.

Did you know?

The production of slate is a very wasteful business due to the very friable nature of the rock. One ton of usable slate could result in up to 35 tons of waste. At the industry's height, Welsh quarries were extracting half a million tons of slate a year, so that's a lot of waste!

Two quarrymen tipping slate waste high above Blaenau Ffestiniog with further massive evidence of tipping behind them. Slate waste is another of the amazing landscape legacies of the industry.

5
Industrial Relations – Slate Lives

The quarrymen lived hard lives – there was no Health and Safety during the operational period of many quarries, and the risks were great. Explosions, falls, dust and collisions with machinery and transport systems were all everyday hazards. There was a general assumption that health and safety was the individual's responsibility, with fatalistic Methodist quarrymen accepting that they were in God's hands at work! Yet by and large, the life of slate workers seems to have been satisfactory depending on the fairness of the employer. The largest dispute was the Penrhyn lockout of 1900. On 22 November 1900 began what was to become the longest-lasting dispute in the industrial history of Britain – the three-year strike by the men of the Penrhyn quarry, Bethesda. On that day in November, some 2,800 men walked out of the quarry. Most would not return for three years, by which time they had been crippled by the wealth and might of the owner, Lord Penrhyn.

Though it is customary to describe the dispute as a strike, it was essentially a lockout as, after walking out en masse, the men were refused entry to the quarry. The dispute was the culmination of several years of dissatisfaction and unrest in the quarrying industry. Chief among concerns was the issue of the 'bargain'. The bargain system protected the quarrymen's earnings against the difficulties of working with rock of variable quality; the system allowed the quarrymen to regard themselves as contractors rather than employees. Disputes had centred on the bargain in 1874, leading to the formation of the North Wales Quarrymen's Union (NWQU), and again in 1896. Unionism was relatively weak in the industry; the NWQU often struggled to recruit more than a third of the workforce to its ranks. However, the Union's leader, W. J. Parry, was well-respected and an important leader of men.

The quarry owner, Lord Penrhyn, and his agent, E. A. Young, had been fighting against the unionisation of their workforce for several years. They were determined upon breaking the tradition of 'bargain' because of the autonomy it afforded the workers. The pair vehemently opposed union strength and it was this right to an effective union that became the main bone of contention during the strike. It was a bitter dispute, with the differences between Penrhyn and his workforce coming to the fore: the wealthy, Anglican, English-speaking landlord versus the working, Nonconformist, predominantly monoglot Welsh quarrymen.

It was against this background that the men of the Penrhyn quarry walked out in November 1900. By 1902, 700 had returned to work, while some 1,300 had left the area in search of work, most to the South Wales coalfield. Tensions between the community and strike-breakers were high and the houses of striking men displayed cards with the words *Nid oes Bradwr yn y Tŷ Hwn* ('There is no traitor in this house') in the window. Slowly but surely, however, the quarrymen were forced back to work in order to feed their families and pay their rents. Despite the large funds collected by sympathetic workforces across Britain, the pressure of being out of work told on the quarrymen and the cards were removed from windows. This exacerbated tension within the community and the atmosphere became increasingly severe during the last months as it became increasingly obvious that Lord Penrhyn would not be defeated.

The strike was a terrible blow to the slate industry. Penrhyn's labour force had decreased to 1,800 by 1907 and a depression in the building industry meant the further contraction of the slate industry. Never again would a strike of this magnitude be seen in the slate industry and of course it was pivotal in developing working relations thereafter. That said, in 1985 to 1986 there was a seven-month strike at the Ffestiniog Slate Company's quarries in Blaenau Ffestiniog over pay cuts and fair pay for female workers that was just as divisive as the Penrhyn lockout. It is not easy to define the role of women in the earlier strikes, but there is no doubt about the part they played during this dispute. During the Miners' Strike of 1984–85 the women of Blaenau had been instrumental in sending food parcels by the score down to the coal miners of southern Wales. Now, the miners' wives were reciprocating in kind to the strikers' families at Blaenau Ffestiniog. Incredible support was given to the strike by institutions and individuals and nearly a thousand letters of support were received. Added to this were the weekly Saturday morning street collections undertaken at Bangor, Caernarfon, Aberystwyth and Cardiff. The strike ended quickly in March 1986 but showed that the quarry workers were still a force to be reckoned with.

Conditions in the quarries were life-threatening as the quarrymen were suspended from ropes along the rock face and used explosives to remove large slabs of rock. If they did not suffer loss of limb or life, many quarrymen developed silicosis as tiny particles of dust from splitting slates settled in their lungs.

At its height in 1898 16,766 men were employed in North Wales alone in the slate industry, a quarter of those working underground in the Blaenau mines. The Cornish Delabole quarry was employing 1,000 men at the same time. The smaller Cumbrian mines were numerous but employed up to a hundred at locations like Honister; multiplied across the region, this

Imagine hundreds of men swarming around the workings of Delabole quarry. While the quarry is still open today, the use of machinery and modern transport methods means the workforce is much smaller.

A view into the workshops at Honister where craft products are made shows much that would be familiar over the last century. Honister continues as a major player in the local economy of the North Lakes.

too ran into the thousands. Even in the twenty-first century, with mechanisation and the contraction of the industry, it is still a major player in the economy of the areas where the quarries are active – and some formerly closed workings have reopened as modern technology has made operation viable once more.

Accommodation for the men near or at the quarry was a feature of the Welsh aspect of the industry not found elsewhere in the British Isles. Fairly cramped industrial housing in two-storey terraces was reasonably commonplace and a number have survived in ruinous form to the present day. At the remote Rhiwbach quarry, there was even a school, the only occasion one was provided as otherwise most barracks were moderately close to civilisation. Often the remains are stark reminders of the living conditions that were tolerated as families strove to win a living from the land and are a surprising piece of Victorian industrial domesticity in the form of terraced houses among the mountains.

Settlements grew up near the quarries where the geography allowed; some were haphazard, others planned where a village didn't already exist. The village of Delabole in Cornwall only really came into existence after three hamlets merged into each other with the growth of the quarry and the coming of the railway. Deinolen, near the Vaynol estate's Dinorwig quarry, was built speculatively by David Griffith on a freehold surrounded by the estate and is planned with terraces and right on the periphery is the chapel – Nonconformism being

Many Welsh quarries were a major distance from any centres of population, so they built housing for the workers to live in. The two terraces at Rhosydd are typical of the kind of accommodation provided, basic but secure from the elements.

rife among the quarry community. On the estate land some distance from the village itself is the Anglican church and a Methodist chapel – standing in splendid isolation in advance of an expansion of the village which never came. Bethesda on the other hand grew up initially unplanned, but by the mid to late nineteenth century, some very large and well thought out developments were created on organised layouts. In Llandegai, plots were leased to quarry workers for thirty years on the condition that they themselves built houses on an approved design. When the leases expired, the houses and the land reverted to the Penrhyn estate – unbridled capitalist exploitation! The house design was adopted in the 1790s by the then Penrhyn estate agent, Benjamin Wyatt, and with successive improvement and enlargement, hundreds of these dwellings were built as the favoured type for the next eighty years.

Some quarries were large enough to provide welfare facilities, perhaps the best known being Dinorwig quarries, which had a hospital. The hospital was built in the 1860s and was largely maintained by the men's own contributions to a Sick Club. The club provided free medical care, a weekly payment during absence from work through sickness or injury, a small payment on retirement and burial expenses. It was one of the first buildings in the area to have hot and cold running water and electricity. General surgery continued here until the 1940s, when the hospital was downgraded to a first aid centre. It closed in 1962 and was later restored by Gwynedd County Council, reopening as a visitor centre in 1979. Apart from the quarry doctor, the staff lived on the premises. The hospital had one of the earliest X-ray machines in North Wales. In the post-mortem room, which was situated in the basement, the table was made from a polished slate slab, complete with channels and drainage holes.

Above: The village of Deinolen is best appreciated from the road leading to Dinorwig quarry where one can see the planned community on the left, with the Anglican church to the middle right and Methodist chapel to the far right.

Below: Chapel was a major part of the life of the quarry community. Capel y Gorlan served Cwmorthin, Conglog and Rhosydd quarries, located right in the heart of Cwmorthin itself. Seen in 1995, it is even more ruinous in 2019.

Quarry hospitals were few and far between; this is the former Oakley quarry hospital in Blaenau Ffestiniog, nestling below the tips of the quarry behind it.

Health and nutrition were key concerns during the nineteenth century, and dust was a killer. More men died in the poor conditions of Welsh slate mines per hundred than their compatriots in the South Wales coal mines. Poor diet also didn't help, bread and stewed tea being the staples – and the tannin in tea lined men's stomachs, preventing essential nutrients being digested. This was particularly what happened in the more remote quarries where the workforce stayed in barracks during the week, only returning home at the weekend. The cases of illness in the Caernarvon and Denbighshire Asylum due to strongly stewed tea are documented in the county records and the Dinorwig quarry doctor noted in his four guidance points for a healthy life that as well as washing and changing clothes, there was 'No goodness in tea!' Research had found that by denying some of the ill patients of the drink, their well-being returned.

Culture was no stranger to the workforce. In Wales, the caban, the cabin where the quarrymen gathered for their lunch break, was often the scene of wide-ranging discussions, which were often formally minuted. A surviving set of minutes from a caban at Llechwedd in Blaenau Ffestiniog records discussions on Church Disestablishment, tariff reform and other political topics. The physical form of a caban could be a slab-walled hut on the tip or a blocked off level far below ground. They developed into a traditional institution, with strict rules about who could speak and when. Although maintaining a formal atmosphere, the assemblies were promoting self-education among the men while counselling and religion also raised their heads. From 1949 to 1964, the Oakley Quarry management published *Caban*, a magazine by and about the quarries in their operation, and this was printed two or three times a year.

Fifty years after closure and despite thousands of people finding the remains, there are still boots, coats and teapots in one of the caban of Dinorwig quarry.

Elsewhere, away from the workplace, music and poetry were favoured pastimes, and the festival of the Eisteddfodd had many quarrymen enter and win prizes. Literature and choirs featured prominently, and fame came to many. Their stories are legion, and Llechwedd quarry tells of but one, David Francis, the blind harpist who lived in a house on the quarry site from 1862 to 1929, whilst Kate Roberts, a quarryman's daughter, rose to prominence as a Welsh language writer and novelist through the twentieth century.

The skills of a quarryman were highly sought after, and men moved across the country in search of work. In extreme cases in the hard times, entire families travelled across the world, taking their craft with them. Welsh miners went to Cornwall and Cumbria, and not just skills went, but ideas and technology. The Greaves slate dressing machine shows the transferability of practices, while other developments such as the use of the narrow-gauge railways spread far and wide.

Did you know?

Celebrations of coronations, weddings and birthdays were marked by quarrymen with the firing of a rock cannon. Holes were drilled into rock and explosive charges detonated in sequence, sometimes leaving a decorative pattern too. One of the most recent firings was to celebrate the sixtieth birthday of the eminent slate historian Dr Michael Lewis.

The holes in the foreground are the rock cannon fired above Penmorfa on the occasion of a Greaves family of Llechwedd's wedding at Wern Manor.

6
The Uses of Slate

As well as the expected use outside as roofing, slate was also used in the nineteenth century as decoration inside cottages. Other uses are for billiard and snooker tables as slate will not distort with heat, and since it withstands acid, it was used for laboratory bench tops and for brewing containers. And not forgetting of course as doorposts, lintels, steps, fencing and water tanks as well as writing slates for schools. There have been many other applications for this versatile and decorative material, not all expected. Slate has been used for baking stones and as a fine insulating material, electric switchboards have been made out of slab – much safer as well than the asbestos ones that often supplanted them.

At Penrhyn there was a further use of slate. After the First World War a by-product of slate quarrying was developed in finely graded slate powder, given the trade name 'Fullersite'. This was used as a filler for things such as road asphalt mixed with bitumen. It was also used in paint making and on felt roofs – there is still a paint manufacturer based in Bethesda to this day. The bagged product was conveyed from the quarry on the Penrhyn Railway in a fleet of four-wheeled wagons designed specifically for the purpose. Decorative aggregate is still shipped from Penrhyn in the twenty-first century.

There has been a tradition in the slate communities of carving slate. Competitions have been held at eisteddfodau for hobbyists wishing to compete. In addition to the local tradition of hobbyists within the community working with slate, there is a significant arts and crafts sector which uses slate as its raw material. Most of the artists and craft workers in the sector are based in, or originated from, the Welsh slate areas. Some of the slate companies

Slate craft has been a popular sideline in the industry since it began. Slate fans such as this show the skill of the individual; this one was bought by the author's parents when Llechwedd opened as a tourist attraction in 1972. Thousands have probably been made since!

attempted to diversify into the sector or have used this as a means of adding glamour to the material. Most of those involved in the slate art and crafts sector are very small, often one-person, enterprises. From Cumbria to Cornwall, there is a thriving small industry producing clocks, wine racks, house signs and coasters among other things. Keswick and Blaenau Ffestiniog have shops in the towns which provide such wares, while the quarries at Honister, Delabole and Llechwedd also have their own retail outlets. The author and his wife bought a Cumbrian slate clock for their engagement while on holiday in Keswick, just one from many made for the tourist trade.

Slate enamelling was very popular by the early 1880s and many prizes were offered at the National Eisteddfod held at Caernarfon in 1880 itself. The winner of the silver medal and prize of £2.00 for carving a tablet of slate 36 inches by 14 inches with a motto on it was Edward Jones, of Bangor. A slate table with a carving of Caernarfon Castle on it was presented for the state room of the chief officer of the training ship *Clio* moored in the Menai Strait, because the ship's band had played at the festival.

In Leeds Art Gallery the landscape artist Richard Long's work called *Delabole Slate 1980* is on display, a circular piece made up of many bits of slate from the Cornish quarry. It was part of the Contested Ground exhibition and is now in a display called the Sculpture Collections, its raw edges and colours contrasting starkly with the clean surroundings of the gallery it resides in. This follows the artist's *Slate Circle* from the previous year made out of Snowdonian slate and displayed in the Tate Gallery in London and was followed by *Cornish*

Keswick town centre has a shop dedicated to the sale of slate goods, house numbers and names and wine racks being popular. It's also a way to use some of the waste material that cannot be used for other purposes.

Leeds Art Gallery is home to *Delabole Slate 1980*, the work of Richard Long, who has created several art works from slate from various sources.

Honister slate craftsmen were working on this cycle and cyclist sculpture in August 2018, to be mounted on completion at the entrance to the mine.

Slate Ellipse in 2009. Long has created several other slate sculptures which are on public exhibition in the UK and around the world as well as more in private collections, showing the versatility of the material in the art world. There are countless other artists working in slate, whether it be as sculpture or as a medium for other works such as paint. At Honister Mine, there are slate sculptures standing guardian to the entrance to the mine from the Honister Pass road, while the summer of 2018 saw the craftsmen there creating a slate cyclist – such is the versatility and attractiveness of the stone.

Did you know?

Art treasures from the National Gallery were stored underground in Manod during the Second World War. The access road under the railway line needed to be dug out lower to allow the lorries with some of the larger canvasses to get to the quarry, where an extensive underground store was created with specially built narrow-gauge railway wagons. Children's author Frank Cottrell-Boyce used this as the inspiration for his book *Framed*.

7

What's Left and the Industry Today

While the peak of the slate industry in the UK could be said to have been just before the First World War, the extractive nature of the operation has left a massive landscape legacy in terms of remains, relics and slate tips. In recent years, there has begun to be a programme of tip removal and processing, with the waste being crushed for use as road surfacing and similar uses. This has been particularly successful in the Blaenau Ffestiniog and Aberllefenni areas of Gwynedd, where thousands of tons have been re-worked. This has resulted in a mixed reception from landscape archaeologists and industrial historians, but as with the quarries that are still in production, continued economic use can only be a good thing for local employment. The landscape of the country continues to evolve – remember that some of the land on the Penrhyn estate was hunting ground before it was part of the quarry for example.

Further landscape changes have occurred in North Wales, where continued production and extraction has resulted in the untopping of old workings, meaning that the roof has been

The reworking of slate tips for road surfacing has continued to shape the landscape of slate quarrying areas. At Aberllefenni in Mid-Wales, the main mine still towers up the hill behind, but the tips in the valley floor are being crushed and removed in this view from June 2017.

A view down the Vale of Ffestiniog from Llechwedd illustrates the massive legacy of the industry, with the town of Blaenau Ffestiniog in the distance and Oakeley quarry tips to the right and Llechwedd to the left. Llechwedd's power station is the slate-roofed building to the right of the main road.

taken off long worked-out galleries to allow good slate to be made. In a similar way, at other quarries in the region, the continued production has once again resulted in the loss of some historic surface features – buildings and transport systems in particular – but the balance of keeping history against keeping people in gainful employment does not always sit easily with some members of the community. The ongoing economic challenges of operating a slate extraction business have given rise to some very imaginative diversification in the last four decades. From Cornwall to Cumbria, slate mines remain in operation, many with some new sidelines to ensure investment and growth into the twenty-first century. From extreme sports to hotel accommodation, there have been many different innovations for visitors to enjoy. Much has been experience-based, the incredible zip wire across Penrhyn quarry being spectacular and high-speed – though the author has yet to be persuaded to try it. In Cumbria at Honister, there are a range of exploration experiences, the Via Ferrata being an inspirational and engaging route up the track of a former slate tramway, taking in many of the historical remains of the mine along the way. Mine tours are also a popular experience – who doesn't like the idea of a visit into the bowels of the earth? Surface tours by lorry operate at a number of sites as well, making accessible the hitherto hidden world of the quarrymen using modern roads driven to access current workings. The Slate Mountain Adventure at Blaenau Ffestiniog is but one of these ventures. At the other end of the spectrum, one can now go 'glamping' at Llechwedd, and the former quarry owners' house has been converted into high-class accommodation.

The Welsh Government building in Cardiff Bay makes extensive use of blue and grey walling and paving from the current Cwt-y-Bugail quarry near Blaenau Ffestiniog (actually the renamed Manod quarry). Even in February 2019, much use is made of Welsh slate where

Above: The working levels of Llechwedd are clear to see, along with the vast waste tips and further quarries behind. There are thousands of tons of waste in this photo alone!

Below: Berwyn quarry at dusk nestles just above the Horseshoe Pass road and shows just how rural an industry slate extraction and processing can be. An old tramway exit incline can just be seen, running top right to bottom centre.

its enduring qualities and aesthetic appeal are important. 60,000 slates were delivered that month as part of the programme to rebuild the roof of Hull railway station – it is coincidental that the great historian of the slate industry, Dr Michael Lewis, is a resident of the city! Elsewhere across the UK, the demand for English and Welsh slate continues and while the industry no longer employs tens of thousands, it does occupy significant proportions of upland populations. The contrast between the agricultural Dee Valley, the Horseshoe Pass and the Berwyn quarry above Llangollen makes this clear. Operating since the mid-nineteenth century, it has always rubbed shoulders with the land around it, and in complete difference to other extractive industries, the quarry sits easily with the hills and bracken around it. While it is not a major extractive site, the workings have been reopened in recent decades and the quarry manages to make a small but significant contribution to the local economy.

Did you know?

The constant temperature underground of six to seven degrees centigrade has allowed an amazing diversification at the Llechwedd quarry, where old workings over 500 feet below the surface have found a new lease of life. A worked-out cavern dating back to 1856 has been fitted out to allow cheese to be aged there in perfect conditions before being sent out to supermarkets across the country. Marketed as 'Slate Quarry Aged', the cheese has given Llechwedd a further string to its bow as well as the popular tourist train into the Deep Mine Experience and the innovative Bounce Below underground trampoline.

Underground, slate quarries remain at a constant temperature, just right for aging cheese! A novel diversification for Llechwedd in recent years, using worked-out chambers.

8
What Now?

Slate quarries and mines are fascinating places, but also dangerous. Rock falls can happen without warning. Underground exploration is hazardous if you have never done it before or are without an experienced guide. In some parts of the country, underground workings have been susceptible to collapse when several thousand tons of roof has given way and caved in. However, done properly, with good equipment and guides, it's an incredibly rewarding pastime. The same goes for surface exploration. There are several locations where organised underground visits can be made. While innovation has been all the rage lately, with zip wires and trampolines, the conventional experience can at least be had in Cumbria and North Wales. Honister mine still operates full mine tours where the remains and current workings underground are accessible daily, while in Snowdonia, the long-running Quarry Tours Deep Mine Experience is operated by the Llechwedd enterprise. Visitors access 150-year-old workings after travelling 500 feet down on a funicular railway and are able to see the caverns for themselves. On a more personal scale, in southern Gwynedd, a range of tours are offered by the Corris Mine Explorers enterprise, which offers a range of underground tours allowing for time, age and experience. These are undertaken in the once vast array of tunnels and chambers that formed the Braich Goch quarry, although

The inclined Deep Mine tour at Llechwedd allows safe access to historic workings for thousands each year and explains the hard working life of the slate miner.

parts of that are also incorporated in the 'King Arthur's Labyrinth' tourist experience, which is completely family-orientated and does not take into account the history of the chambers the displays occupy. The entrance to both tours is located at the Corris Craft Centre, which is a modern development on the site of the mills for Braich Goch. While there are no tangible surface remains at ground level, there is a very comprehensive and readable display on the quarries of the Dulas Valley in which the attraction is situated. Carnglaze caverns, Cornwall's only slate mine, facilitates a self-guided tour of the three chambers that make up the mine. If one so desires, Carnglaze is also licenced to hold weddings underground – certainly a venue with a difference!

The recent potential classification of the slate region of Gwynedd as a World Heritage Site has encouraged further celebration of the remains of the industry and several walks and trails have been published for the general visitor. These range from short walks of a mile or so to the formally instituted Snowdonia Slate Trail, which takes in 80 miles, a number of slate mining districts and can only be accomplished in four days or more. The Forestry Commission has also created a trail around the former Bryn Eglwys quarry which is easily traceable even without a guide or map. At Bryn Eglwys, around the route are listening posts and interpretation panels which explain where the walker is and what they are seeing – powered by wind-up electricity, they offer a more accessible insight into heavily overgrown landscapes. A positive of course for these routes is that they are proven and on public rights of way. The enormity of Dinorwig can be appreciated from part of the Slate Trail as it traverses the middle of the quarry from one end to the other, passing open pits, galleries and inclines on the route, as well as possessing a view point. This latter overlooks Llyn Padarn, the hydroelectric power station and town of Llanberis but turning around 180 degrees allows one to take in the full spectacle and size of the Dinorwig enterprise.

In the Corris area, the Centre for Alternative Technology has recently opened a walk around Escairgeiliog quarry, in which it is based. There are guided tours or one can wander by oneself, in which case the interpretation panels and relics are very helpful and provide a fascinating hour.

Just some of the attractions and walks relating to slate heritage, from the strenuous and exhilarating to gentle investigation. Why not try something?

Walking old slate quarries is a great family experience; a number have trails or footpaths around, such as Bryn Eglwys. The Forestry Commission have worked to provide access, seen being enjoyed by the author's wife Kathryn and youngest daughter Charlotte in April 2009.

The vastness of the former Dinorwig quarry can easily and safely be appreciated from the accessible path through the middle of the site. It now forms part of the Snowdonia Slate Trail and is popular with walkers and cyclists alike.

Many quarries themselves are on private land and while they can be accessed in Cumbria, Wales and Cornwall, they are still inherently dangerous, and one visits at one's own risk. The lorry or four-by-four vehicle tours offered by a few places give a safe way of getting to some of the further reached remains while remaining out of the way of current operations or some of the riskier parts of a quarry. Working quarries such as Buttermere, Burlington and Penrhyn are so busy that there is no possible access at all. Modern large equipment operates with state-of-the-art control and extraction systems, while the mills in which the slate is processed are likewise computer-controlled and have very advanced dust extraction systems. Delabole allows tours with viewing from a special area on weekdays during the summer season, though prior booking can be used to gain privileged access to the working pit of the quarry. There are visitor centres at Llechwedd and Honister while the slate works of Inigo Jones at Groeslon gives an insight into production of slate ware.

In terms of museums, the major player is the Welsh Slate Museum at Llanberis, in the shadow of the Dinorwig quarry. Based in the former Gilfach Ddu workshops, and part of the National Museums and Galleries of Wales, it was opened after the closure of Dinorwig in 1969. It covers not just the preservation of the workshops – machine shop, foundry and woodwork shop – but also slate production, transport and the social and economic impact of the industry. There are live demonstrations of slate splitting and dressing, and outside, a row of terraced houses from Blaenau Ffestiniog has been re-erected, with each house representing a different period from the history of the industry. Elsewhere as part of the complex (which also includes the Llanberis Lake Railway), there is the preserved quarry

At Llechwedd, the tourist operation sits alongside the working quarry well. The attraction can be seen in the left and middle of the photo, while the still working mills are above in the middle and to the right, an arrangement that works and shows the integration of the operation.

Gordon and Ann Hatherill's children explore the giant lathe in the workshops at the Welsh Slate Museum at Gilfach Ddu in the old Dinorwig quarry complex.

hospital, a self-acting incline for transport of slate and a short walk into the small Vivian quarry, which has a Blondin cable lift rebuilt over the quarry pit itself. The Lake Railway has been rebuilt along part of the original Padarn Railway which ran to Port Dinorwic, which today is a marina with sailing club – but retains its identity as Y Felinheli to keep the link with the past alive. Several of the narrow-gauge railways whose roots lie in the industry have been revived either in part or in whole, and each has its own museum reflecting the slate origins of the lines – notable among these being the Ffestiniog, Talyllyn, Corris and Welsh Highland – and an internet search will provide opening times and details of the heritage facilities at each line. In Porthmadog, the Maritime Museum pays tribute to the ships, shipbuilders and sailors who transported the slate to the wider market across the world – sited across the harbour from the terminus station of the Ffestiniog Railway, the legacy of distribution is clear to see and easily understandable. Across the town, the museum of the Welsh Highland Heritage Railway displays material from the Fforwm Plas Tan y Bwlch and is very close to 'Y Cyt' (The Cut), allegedly a former canal, now a drainage channel, which pre-dated the railway to link Porthmadog Harbour with Tremadog. The whole town of Porthmadog is a legacy to the joint heritage of the slate industry and the town's creator, William Madocks; however, that's a story one can find out by visiting and spending a day or more in the area!

If geography, ability or other practicalities preclude the active exploration of quarries and their remains or the associated landscape and infrastructure, there are dozens of published sources, books and pamphlets. The original in-depth history is Dr Jean Lindsay's book on

A wonderful example of community interest in the past can be seen in July and August each year when the Blaenau Ffestiniog Heritage Centre opens in the high street. A selection of artefacts and images along with recollections from the volunteers who run the centre can easily lead to a captivating hour or so.

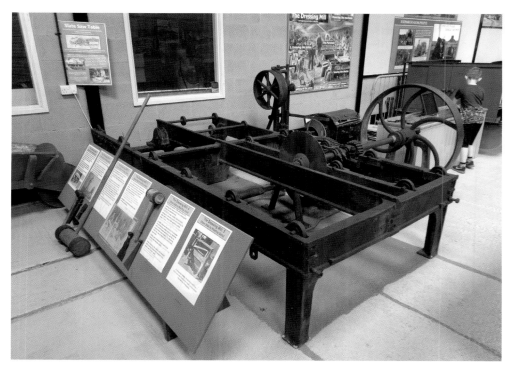

In Porthmadog, the museum at the Welsh Highland Heritage Railway displays not only railway material but a number of items collected by members of Fforwm Plas Tan y Bwlch, who actively study and record the slate industry of the area.

Leicestershire no long has any public exhibition of its slate workings; until 2015, the Extractive Gallery at Snibston Discovery Museum had a display of Swithland slate and its processing.

The Welsh Highland Heritage Museum also shows material from the Ffestiniog Railway, including this wooden slate wagon and dandy cart from the gravity slate trains. Similar slate railway heritage can now also be found at the Bala Lake Railway interpretation centre.

History of the North Wales Slate Industry from the 1970s; other regions have yet to have a single title covering them in entirety, though a number of recent books have begun to look at Cumbrian slate holistically. The studies of individual quarries, mines, communities and aspects of the industry are legion. Cornwall's Delabole has a thick tome which draws out the inextricable link between the quarry and the village, while David Ramsay in the Midlands has produced the only two known publications covering the lesser-known Swithland slate in Leicestershire. It is Wales and Cumbria which dominate the bookshelves however, and the names of Ian Tyler in the North West, and Alun John Richards in Wales who have been most prolific, Alun also extended his work to the quarries of Pembrokeshire as well. The late Ivor Wynne Jones concentrated on a number of titles focusing solely on the Greaves family and the Llechwedd quarry, spanning a publication period of four decades. In recent times, the Welsh situation has been drawn together by the magnum opus of Dr David Gwyn, whose magisterial book *Welsh Slate* has rightly drawn praise and awards and deserves a place on the shelves of anyone with an interest in the region. On an international scale, the American publication *The Slate Roof Bible* covers the whole of the UK but also places it into context with the quarries and techniques across the world – and gives a great and detailed insight into the craft of roofing itself with the material. Many other books concentrate on individual quarries, technologies, transport and people – some of these being quite limited in print numbers and always worth seeking out – such as the diaries of Moses Kellow. Former quarry manager Fred Hughes of Porthmadog has also studied the foundries supplying the industry with equipment – all aspects which flesh out the wider picture and show that slate did not exist in microcosm but affected the world around it in so many ways. The social and economic side of the industry has been addressed by authors such as Merfyn Williams, who documented the growth and work of the North Wales Quarrymen's Union, and in recent times the superb local studies of Bryn Eglwys and Corris by Sara Eade.

The study of the industry continues, and more is learned every year. The study and recording courses held each year at Plas Tan y Bwlch – the Snowdonia National Park Study Centre – being particularly well-established institutions. The recording courses were begun by Dr Michael Lewis, another pioneer of study into the industry, and are now led by Dr David Gwyn. The results are deposited in the Caernarvonshire Record Office where they form a growing resource documenting and recording the past of the region. The author spent a week on one of these courses in 1996 and was privileged to be working on the Pen yr Orsedd quarry, where we also benefitted from the input of the late Dr Gwynfor Pierce Jones, whose knowledge and practical experience were encyclopaedic. The Plas also became home to Fforwm Plas Tan y Bwlch – a group of local historians and quarrymen including the late Griff Jones and Dafydd Price who investigated and published further. They continue to meet to study, discuss and disseminate knowledge of the industry, its techniques, tools and people. Some of their artefacts are on display at the Welsh Highland Heritage Railway in Porthmadog. There are few societies or clubs completely devoted to slate other than the Fforwm, but organisations such as the Welsh Mines Society, the Association for Industrial

Slate industry reading is many and varied, from in-depth histories of one region to photographic records of specific quarries. New and second-hand titles provide plenty of books to fill dark winter evenings!

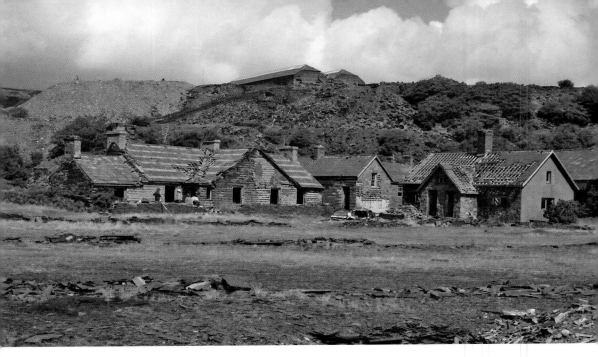

Practical Industrial Archaeology is a long-running course run by Plas Tan y Bwlch. In August 1996, the author spent a week on one of the courses, recording parts of Pen yr Orsedd quarry during their closed holiday week. Some of the group are here seen measuring the former quarry offices which they will later draw up and write about.

During the Plas Tan y Bwlch course, fascinating things come to light, including much graffiti scratched into stone by quarrymen. Something different was the wall paintings on of one of the former incline winding houses.

Archaeology or the Cumbrian Amenity Trust Mining History Society cater for those whose interest includes quarrying and mining. Most of these organisations also have websites, while there are several websites dedicated to slate in particular. The most comprehensive Welsh site is Dave Sallery's www.penmorfa.com/slate where there is a superb selection of images past and present, studies of quarries and the legacy of the industry. There are also online surveys of quarries and many pictures on such sites as Flickr. Discussion of all aspects of mines and quarries can be found at www.mine-explorer.co.uk from recommended equipment for underground exploration to sales of books and notes on the current state of sites all across the UK. www.aditnow.co.uk is a similar resource, also with copious albums of images and chat forums as part of the content – well worth a few hours' browsing on dark winter evenings. Many films, both past and present, can be found on YouTube, a great resource allowing one to visit locations from one's own front room. Links to a lot of these and more are a feature also of the Facebook page Slate Quarry Enthusiasts, set up by the author when it was noted that there were pages for all kinds of subject but none for the slate industry.

A further, more intimate way to enjoy the industry is to make a model of aspects of it. Branching out often from the activity of model railways, many layouts have incorporated a quarry as part of their scenery. In the last thirty-five years, there has been a growing interest in modelling quarries in their own right. One can have a small version of Dinorwig or Penrhyn

Internet discussion of slate quarries led the author to Goleuwern slate quarry on the coast of Cardigan Bay. Barmouth is seen in the distance and there are several interesting remains, including an old winding drum in the foreground.

At Maenofferen, the locomotive running wagons to the incline head would sometimes be set off on its own with the driver walking ahead or alongside like a horse. In 2014, the author recreated this in 16 mm scale with his Ruston loco and wagons on the Talyllyn Railway's garden railway, which incorporates parts of the late Peter Jones' slate-inspired line.

in your own home, and the scales vary too. The commonest, which is the normal train set size, 00, now has ready-to-run Hunslet locomotives and wagons, while the kit industry is burgeoning with offers for waste wagons, quarrymen's carriages and even some buildings. This is in addition to the mainstream public railways such as the Talyllyn and Ffestiniog. As the scales increase, there are still kits to be bought, or the art of scratch building, either using parts or making one's one, through 0 gauge scale to 16 mm scale outside in the garden – the author himself had a slate tramway in his late teens and early twenties in his parents' garden. The late Peter Jones of Haverfordwest had a monumental quarry rising several feet and sculpted out of concrete in his back garden. In Surrey, the authors of the classic book *Slate Quarry Album*, Ann and the late Gordon Hatherill, combined their love of narrow-gauge railways with their slate research and built a 5-inch gauge slate tramway with scale buildings in their garden. Elsewhere, several industrial set pieces inspired by certain quarries or parts thereof have been faithfully created and shown around the country, Peter Wilson's *Chwarel Cwm Bach* being an 8-foot-deep recreation of several levels of Dinorwig in 00 or 4mm to the foot scale.

Perhaps the finest legacy to the industry is in the capital of Welsh slate, Blaenau Ffestiniog itself. The town centre has undergone a massive transformation and makeover in recent years. Several slate structures have been built with poetry engraved on them. The structures are roughly 40 feet tall and are intended to visually echo the towering slate